MEGA ROBO
RUMBLE

BY NEILL CAMERON

With additional colouring by
Abby Bulmer and Lisa Murphy

MEGA R... BOOK 2

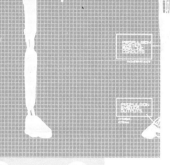

Mega Robo Bros - INTERVIEW

News // UK // Lifestyle & Culture

27 September
by J. Abumrad, staff writer

They're schoolboys. They're brothers. And, as of this week, they are both newly authorised special agents of R.A.I.D. — the international agency for Robotics Analysis, Intelligence and Defence. Today we are very fortunate to feature a rare and exclusive interview with Alex and Freddy Sharma, the "Mega Robo Bros" themselves.

We meet in a cafe on the Mile End Road, Alex (12) and Freddy (6) attended by their adopted parents — R.A.I.D. chief scientific officer Dr Nita Sharma and her husband, Michael Sharma. Michael goes to order coffees for the adults and ice creams for the boys, while I begin talking to Alex and Freddy, conscious all the while of their ⬛ me.

⬛ robots?" I ask.

⬛ arrassed by the inanity ⬛d Alex seems to agree, ⬛ me with a distinctly

⬛ fly, and we are super ⬛so we have lasers!"

AND ABOVE ONLY

on at R.A.I.D. facility 03CA-FF07
⬛nal care of Senior Scientific Officer
⬛ng well, and language
⬛r Sharma's projections,
⬛ommunicative and withdrawn.

⬛that it would be desirable to
⬛tting, with continued observation
⬛E PLAYROOM"), and to begin

⬛ation on the situation of their
⬛that no further attempts at

For Logan. Again. Obviously.

Mega Robo Bros 2: Mega Robo Rumble
is a
DAVID FICKLING BOOK

First published in Great Britain in 2017 by
David Fickling Books,
31 Beaumont Street,
Oxford, OX1 2NP
www.davidficklingbooks.com

Text and illustrations © Neill Cameron, 2017

978-1-910989-81-4

1 3 5 7 9 10 8 6 4 2

The right of Neill Cameron to be identified as the author and illustrator of this work
has been asserted in accordance with the Copyright, Designs and Patents Act 1988.

Papers used by David Fickling Books are from well-managed forests
and other responsible sources.

DAVID FICKLING BOOKS Reg. No. 8340307
A CIP catalogue record for this book is available from the British Library.

Printed and bound in Great Britain by Sterling.

TABLE OF CONTENTS

ST 'ROBOT 23' LIN
EXPLOSION

21 September
by Alix Spiegel, staf

More details are em
the enormous explo
the top 10 floors of
at 4 Canada Place la
It has been confirme
no human casualtie
the incident. Police
that the building's p
uppermost floors we
by the mysterious C
known only as 'Robe
to be responsible fo
on Buckingham Pala
Skyline. The explosi
bomb — apparently
own hand — in whi

Photo: AP

LONDON!

THE FUTURE!

(CURRENTLY UNDER RECONSTRUCTION)

KZOWWW!!!

LOOK OUT! THERE'S ANOTHER ONE!

DEEP BELOW GROUND, THE SECURE HEADQUARTERS OF R.A.I.D. – ROBOTICS ANALYSIS, INTELLIGENCE AND DEFENCE.

I'LL GET IT!

KZOWW!!!

OWWW!

FREDDY!

YOU SHOT ME!

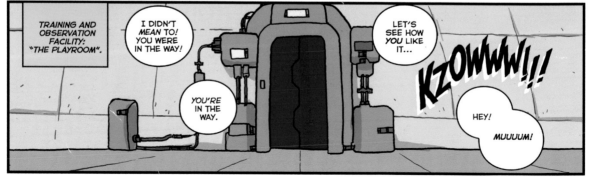

TRAINING AND OBSERVATION FACILITY: "THE PLAYROOM".

I DIDN'T MEAN TO! YOU WERE IN THE WAY!

LET'S SEE HOW YOU LIKE IT...

KZOWWW!!!

YOU'RE IN THE WAY.

HEY!

MUUUUM!

CHAPTER 1:
MEGA ROBO SCHOOLDAYS

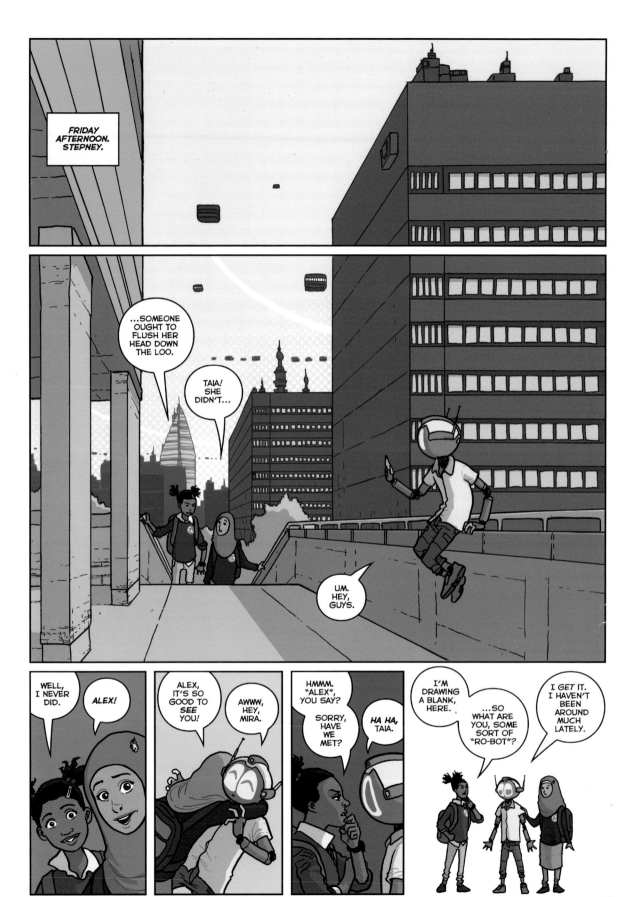

FRIDAY AFTERNOON. STEPNEY.

...SOMEONE OUGHT TO FLUSH HER HEAD DOWN THE LOO.

TAIA! SHE DIDN'T...

UM. HEY, GUYS.

WELL, I NEVER DID.

ALEX!

ALEX, IT'S SO GOOD TO *SEE* YOU!

AWWW, HEY, MIRA.

HMMM. "ALEX", YOU SAY?

SORRY, HAVE WE MET?

HA HA, TAIA.

I'M DRAWING A BLANK, HERE.

...SO WHAT ARE YOU, SOME SORT OF "RO-BOT"?

I *GET* IT. I HAVEN'T BEEN AROUND MUCH LATELY.

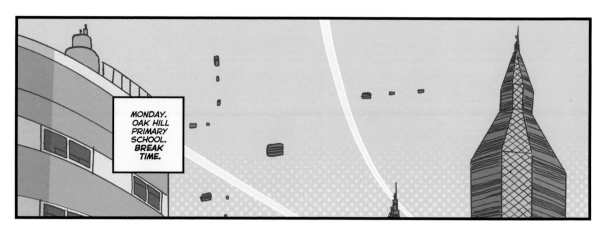

MONDAY. OAK HILL PRIMARY SCHOOL. BREAK TIME.

I COULDN'T BELIEVE IT WHEN ANYA GOT EXPELLED FOR BITING VALERIA...

MIRA! *SPOILERS*, DUDE! I'M ONLY UP TO CHAPTER EIGHT...

OH, YOU'RE NOT *STILL* TALKING ABOUT THE DUMB VAMPIRE BOOK?

IT'S REALLY *GOOD*, TAIA!

IT – OOF!

HA HA HA! *OOPS!*

YOU DID THAT ON PURPOSE, JAMAL!

IT'S *TINHEAD'S* FAULT, FOR NOT GETTING OUT OF THE WAY!

HOW COME YOU'RE ALWAYS HANGING OUT WITH GIRLS ANYWAY, TINHEAD?

ARE YOU ACTUALLY A GIRL OR SOMETHING?

CLEAR OFF, JAMAL.

OH MY GOSH, YOU *ARE*!

YOU'RE STILL A *GIRL.*

A GIRL WHO JUST *KICKED YOUR BOTTOM* AT FOOTBALL.

SUCKS TO BE *YOU.*

ON SO, SO MANY LEVELS.

THANKS, GUYS.

...YOU DO KNOW I'M NOT ACTUALLY A GIRL THOUGH, RIGHT?

OH GOD, AM I A GIRL?

ALEX! GROW SOME HAIR SO WE CAN BRAID IT!

OH, LEAVE HER ALONE.

R.A.I.D. HQ, TUESDAY.

MUM? ARE YOU IN HERE?

ALEX? ARE YOU OKAY?

I'M SORT OF IN THE MIDDLE OF SOMETHING HERE.

UM.

HAVE YOU GOT A MINUTE? TO TALK?

SURE, I CAN TALK WHILE I WORK. WHAT'S UP?

I... WELL, IT'S NOTHING, I JUST...

I DUNNO, THIS GUY AT SCHOOL SAID SOME STUFF.

...AND I KNOW HE'S A MORON, BUT ANYWAY...

...IT JUST... UM.

I WAS JUST WONDERING...

...AM I A BOY OR A GIRL?

I MEAN... I GUESS I ALWAYS JUST SORT OF ASSUMED I WAS A BOY. BUT *AM* I?

AND WHAT DOES THAT *MEAN*, ANYWAY?

UM, WELL...

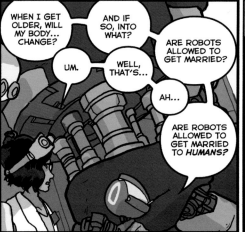

WHEN I GET OLDER, WILL MY BODY... CHANGE?

AND IF SO, INTO WHAT?

UM.

WELL, THAT'S...

ARE ROBOTS ALLOWED TO GET MARRIED?

AH...

ARE ROBOTS ALLOWED TO GET MARRIED TO *HUMANS*?

CAN ROBOTS HAVE BABIES? AND IF SO, HOW?

IS IT THE SAME WAY HUMANS HAVE BABIES? AND HOW DOES THAT WORK, ANYWAY?

WOW, WELL...

TAIA TOLD ME ONCE, BUT I'M PRETTY SURE SHE WAS MAKING IT UP.

AND ALSO...

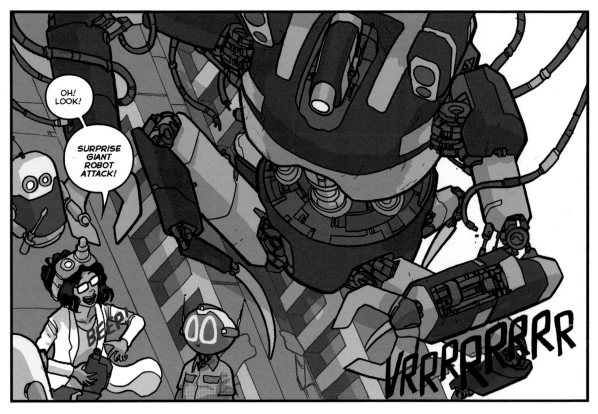

OH! LOOK!

SURPRISE GIANT ROBOT ATTACK!

BEER

VRRRRRRRR

WHAT?

SLAM!

EXIT

MUM!

MUM, YOU SUCK!

I'M SORRY!

YOUR DAD IS REALLY BETTER AT THIS SORT OF THING!

EXIT

15

CHAPTER 2:
MEGA ROBO UNDERGROUND

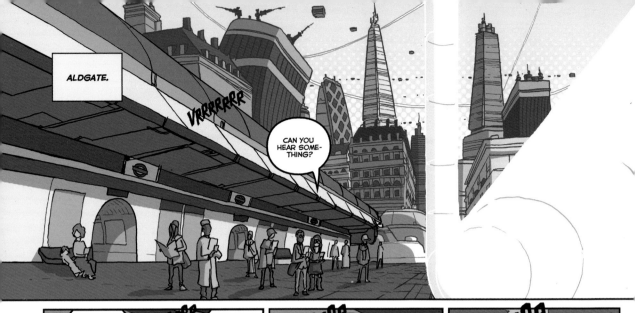

ALDGATE.

VRRRRRR

CAN YOU HEAR SOME-THING?

SORRY, I HAD MY HEADPHONES IN. WHAT?

VRRRRRR

I SAID, CAN YOU HEAR SOME-THING?

VRRRRRR

OH — ENGINEERING WORKS, MAYBE?

I DUNNO, IT SOUNDS PRETTY...

VRRRRRR

KR-SHMM!

DRILL!

DRIILL!!

VRRRRRR

DRIIILL!!!

KSHOOM!!

H...

H...

HELP!!

SOMEBODY HELP!

ALEX? FREDDY? CAN YOU HEAR ME?

HI, MUM!

WHERE ARE WE GOING?

ALDGATE.

I'M JUST SENDING A FLIGHT PLAN TO YOUR A.R. SYSTEMS, HOLD ON...

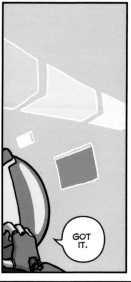

GOT IT.

THANKS, MUM.

SO WHAT ARE WE DEALING WITH?

THERE'S BEEN AN INCIDENT AT THE SKYTUBE TRANSFER STATION – AN ENTIRE SECTION OF THE TRACK'S COLLAPSED.

WOW, LOOK AT THAT GUY!

ONE OF THE PASSENGERS CAPTURED THIS FOOTAGE – THIS WAS NO ACCIDENT, BUT APPEARS TO BE AN ATTACK BY A MODEL 7 INDUSTRIAL DRILL-MECH.

TWO CIVILIANS WERE INJURED, THE REST FLED – BY THE TIME A POLICE RESPONSE TEAM ARRIVED, THE MECH WAS LONG GONE, BACK UNDERGROUND.

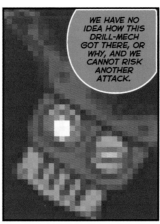

OH, COOL!

IT GOES DOWN INTO THE DISUSED *UNDERGROUND* TUNNELS.

THIS MUST BE THE OLD CENTRAL LINE.

IT'S BEEN CLOSED FOR YEAYS — ALL THE PASSENGERS SWITCHED TO THE SKYLINE...

I CAN'T SEE A *THING* DOWN HERE.

DUDE. JUST TURN YOUR HEADLIGHTS ON.

WAIT, WHAT?!

WE HAVE *HEADLIGHTS?!*

SURE. JUST GO INTO *FUNCTIONS > EXTRAS > LIGHTING* AND SET IT TO 'MAX'...

O...K.?

WAH!

OH WOW!

OH *WOW.*

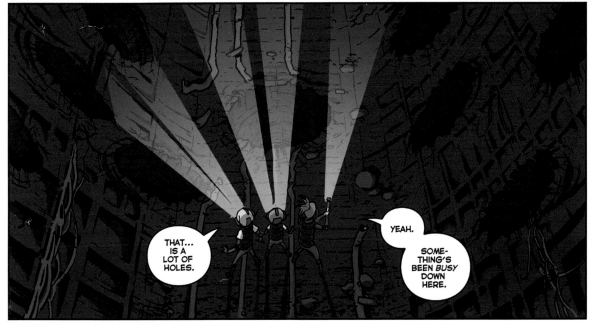

THAT... IS A LOT OF HOLES.

YEAH.

SOME-THING'S BEEN *BUSY* DOWN HERE.

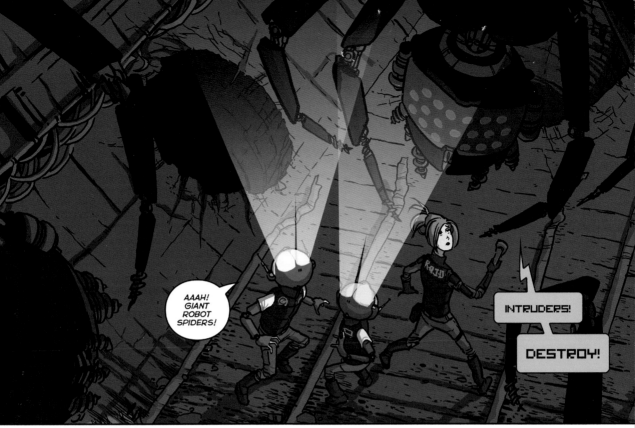

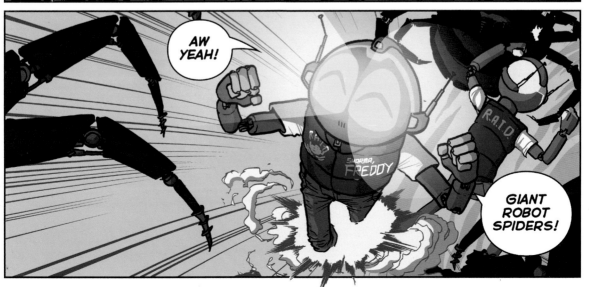

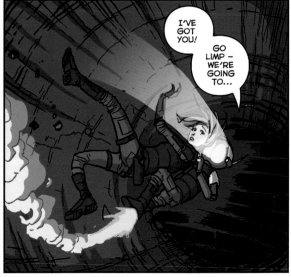

OVERRIDE CODE: *DELTA SIERRA LIMA NINE NINE ZERO.*

SLEEP MODE, EVERYONE.

WHO...?

MY NAME...

YOU DON'T NEED TO KNOW MY NAME.

YOU CAN CALL ME THE CARETAKER.

WELCOME TO THE *SHELTER.*

'SHELTER'? WHERE *ARE* WE?

IT'S AN OLD UNDERGROUND STATION.

AN OLD UNDERGROUND STATION... FULL OF ROBOTS?

SO, WHAT, YOU COLLECT OLD ROBOTS DOWN HERE?

I DON'T COLLECT THEM. I PRESERVE THEM.

I REPAIR THEM.

I *CARE* FOR THEM.

THESE ARE INCREDIBLE PIECES OF ENGINEERING. WORKS OF *ART.*

AND THEY HAVE BEEN ABANDONED. THROWN ON THE SCRAP HEAP.

CAST ASIDE, BECAUSE IT WAS CHEAPER TO REPLACE THEM WITH NEW MODELS.

CAST ASIDE, JUST BECAUSE THEY WERE... "BROKEN".

KROOM!!

YOU SHOULD NEVER HAVE COME HERE.

DESTROY!

DESTROY!

HERE WE GO AGAIN...

AW, YEAH! *GIANT ROBOT SPIDER FIGHT!*

THEY'RE *YOURS*, RIGHT?

YOUR GUARDS? DEFENDING THIS... 'SHELTER'?

YES! DEFENDING IT FROM PEOPLE LIKE *YOU!*

SO *STOP* THEM!

YOU HAVE THE OVERRIDE CODES – SHUT THEM *DOWN!*

NO! THESE ROBOTS ARE MY FRIENDS – MY *FAMILY!*

I WON'T LET YOU *KILL* THEM!

THEY'RE *NOT ALIVE!*

YOU *HAVE* TO SEE THAT!

LOOK, I *KNOW THEY* CAN SEEM... REAL. BUT THEY'RE NOT.

THEY CAN'T THINK FOR THEMSELVES, THEY'RE JUST... *PROGRAMMED.*

THEY'RE JUST... THINGS.

THEY DON'T *FEEL* ANYTHING, OR... *WANT* ANYTHING, OR...

HUH?

I WANT STUFF!

I WANT *LOTS* OF STUFF!

HELLO?

ANYONE?

THEY'RE ALL GONE.

LOOKS LIKE THE 'CARETAKER' TOOK ALL HER ROBOTS AND CLEARED OUT.

AWWW. I LIKED THE TEDDY ONE.

I'LL CALL IN A BACKUP TEAM. WE CAN EXTRACT THE DRILL-MECH WRECKAGE AND START TRACKING DOWN THE REST...

DO WE *HAVE* TO?

WHAT?

I MEAN — WE NEUTRALISED THE DRILL-MECH. THAT WAS OUR OBJECTIVE, RIGHT? THE REST OF THEM WEREN'T HURTING ANYONE. CAN'T WE JUST LET THEM GO?

WHAT'S THE WORST THAT COULD HAPPEN?

...I DON'T *KNOW,* ALEX. I DON'T KNOW.

AND THAT'S WHAT WORRIES ME.

CHAPTER 3:

MEGA ROBO WEEKEND

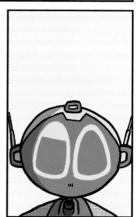

ACTION& ADVENTURE!

FRIENDS & FEELINGS!

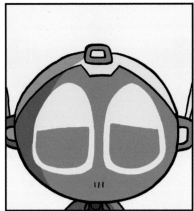

ACTION& ADVENTURE!

FRIENDS & FEELINGS!

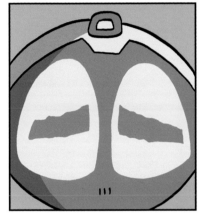

ACTION& ADVENTURE!

FRIENDS & FEELINGS!

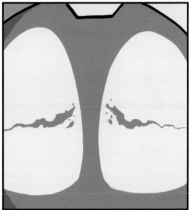

ALEX, COME ON, WE HAVEN'T GOT ALL...

...ALEX?

HEY. *HEY.*

IT'S OKAY.

IT'S OKAY.

I KNOW. I KNOW.

COME ON.

HELL WITH IT. I'LL JUST GET YOU ONE OF EACH.

...WAIT A MINUTE.

HOW COME ALEX GETS *TWO?!*

HOME.

"Man is fully responsible for his nature and his choices."

HA HA! YOU'RE SO FUNNY, STUPID PHILOSOPHY PENGUIN!

"Man is fully responsible for his nature and his choices."

GREAT. GOOD. WELL DONE.

"Man is fully responsible for his nature and his choices."

RUFF!

"Man is fully responsible for his nature and his choices."

BAGUETTE!

"Man is fully responsible for his nature and his choices."

FREDDY! CAN YOU COME AND DO SOMETHING ABOUT YOUR ᑲᕮᕮᕮᕮᑭ! PENGUIN?

"Man is fully responsible for his nature and his choices."

WHY IS THAT THING EVEN HERE?

CAN WE HAVE IT MELTED DOWN?

THE PLAYROOM.

IT'S NOT FAIR!

KRANGG!!!

IT'S NOT FAIR!

KZOMM!!!

IT'S –

NOT –

CHAPTER 4:
MEGA ROBO CELEBRITIES

SCHOOL!

BREAK TIME.

HEY, ALEX?

HUH? OH, HI, JAMILA.

SO I SAW YOU ON TV AGAIN LAST NIGHT! YOU WERE, LIKE, FIGHTING GIANT ROBOTS OR SOMETHING? YOU LOOKED GREAT!

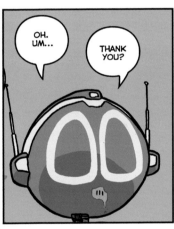

OH. UM...

THANK YOU?

SO YOU'RE, LIKE, FAMOUS NOW?

I MEAN... I GUESS?

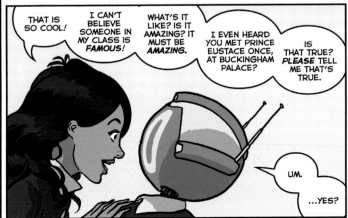

THAT IS SO COOL!

I CAN'T BELIEVE SOMEONE IN MY CLASS IS *FAMOUS!*

WHAT'S IT LIKE? IS IT AMAZING? IT MUST BE *AMAZING.*

I EVEN HEARD YOU MET PRINCE EUSTACE ONCE, AT BUCKINGHAM PALACE?

IS THAT TRUE? *PLEASE* TELL ME THAT'S TRUE.

UM. ...YES?

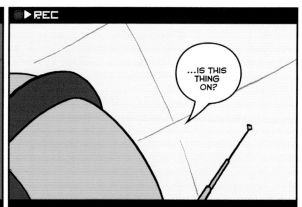

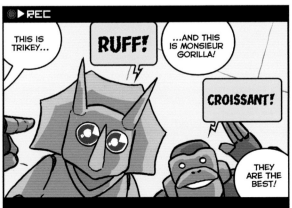

SATURDAY.

THE SCIENCE MUSEUM.

...DO WE *HAVE* TO?

ALEX, WE TALKED ABOUT THIS – BEING ASKED TO OPEN THE NEW *HISTORY OF A.I.* EXHIBITION IS A REAL HONOUR.

BUT... THERE'S GOING TO BE A BIG *CROWD*, ISN'T THERE?

YEAH! IT'S GOING TO BE AWESOME!

AND THEN I'LL GET LIKE A ZILLION NEW SUBSCRIBERS TO MY VUTUBE CHANNEL, AND GET EVEN MORE *FAMOUSER!*

OKAY, THEY'RE READY FOR YOU.

I JUST... I DON'T WANT EVERYONE *LOOKING* AT ME.

WHAT?

I *DO!*

THIS IS *NOT OPTIONAL.* FOR BETTER OR WORSE, YOU TWO ARE THE PUBLIC FACES OF R.A.I.D. NOW...

...HEAVEN HELP US...

AND THAT MEANS DOING THIS KIND OF EVENT SOMETIMES. AND *MAKING A GOOD IMPRESSION.*

ALEX, IT'LL BE OKAY. YOU JUST SAY A FEW WORDS, WAVE AT THE CAMERAS, IT'LL BE OVER IN A FEW MINUTES.

...FINE.

NOTHING TO WORRY...

...ABOUT?

LOOK!

THERE HE IS!

IT'S HIM!

59

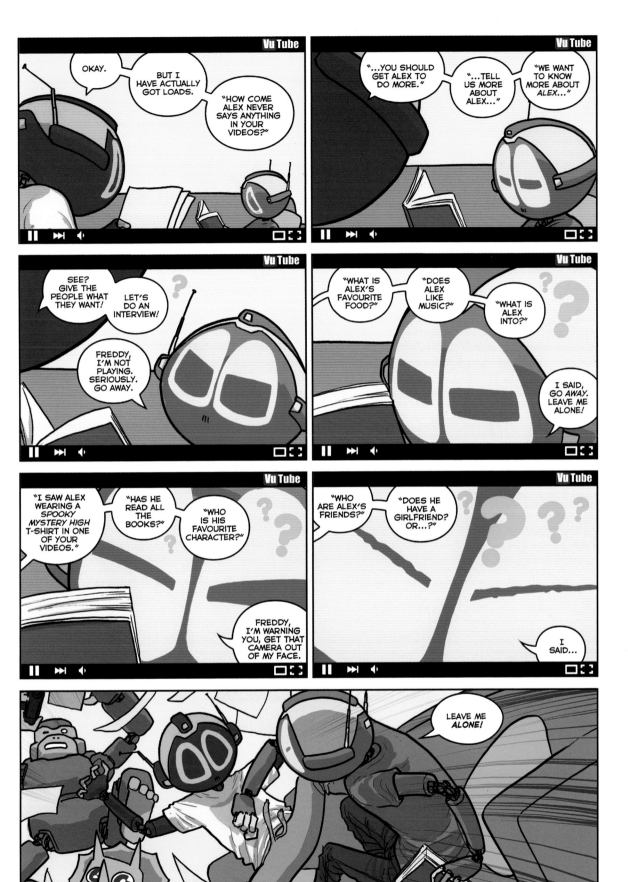

THURSDAY NIGHT.

NEW TELEVISION CENTRE.

...BUT I DON'T *WANT* TO BE ON TELLY!

ALEX, IT'S JUST A SHORT INTERVIEW.

I DON'T *WANT* TO BE INTERVIEWED!

I DON'T WANT TO BE *FAMOUS!*

I JUST WANT TO *GO HOME* AND... AND... *READ A BOOK.*

YOU'RE *SO BORING!*

YOU'RE *BORING.* YOU'RE *JEALOUS* OF MY *INTERNET FAMOUSNESS,* AND YOU'RE *BEING A JERK!*

SHUT UP!

OW! GET OFF!

MUM. *TELL HIM!*

STOP!

JUST... STOP!

I CAN'T TAKE ALL THIS CONSTANT *FIGHTING!*

IF YOU GUYS CAN'T GET ON, I'M GOING TO... TO SHUT THIS *WHOLE THING DOWN!*

SUITS ME.

BUT *DAD!* WHAT ABOUT MY *ADORING PUBLIC?*

OKAY GUYS, YOU'RE ON.

LOOK!

THERE HE IS!

IT'S *HIM!*

SEE? THEY *LOVE* ME!

THEY –

CHAPTER 5:
MEGA ROBO EXPO

WELCOME to **LONDON ROBO EXPO!**

SEVEN FLOORS of all the latest developments in robotics and cybertechnology from around the world!

MEET the latest-model human simulates, so real you won't believe they're not real!

WATCH ferocious battle-mechs engage in GLADIATORIAL COMBAT in the ROBO ARENA!

LISTEN to a series of INTERESTING DISCUSSIONS about the social and political ramifications of...

UGH. *BORING.*

I WANT TO SEE THE *FIGHTING!*

BUT DAAAAD! I CAN HEAR MUM TALK ANY DAY.

THEY HAVE GLADIATOR ROBOTS!

"Three o' clock is always too early or too late for anything you want to do."

...THE PENGUIN.

IT'S NOT ENOUGH I'M LOOKING AFTER FOUR KIDS, WE HAD TO BRING THE

beeeeeeep!

PENGUIN.

WHY DON'T WE SPLIT UP?

WE'LL GO SEE MUM, AND YOU CAN TAKE FREDDY TO HIS DUMB FIGHTING THING.

YOU'RE DUMB!

THANKS, ALEX.

AW YEAH, GLADIATOR ROBOTS!

MEET UP AT THE CAFE AT FOUR, OKAY?

LOOK! DOWN THERE!

ARE THEY...?

THEY ARE.

I DON'T BELIEVE IT.

THE ROBOTICUS PROTOTYPES.

OH, THIS JUST GOT INTERESTING.

...AND WELCOME BACK TO *LONDON ROBO EXPO!*

NEXT UP WE HAVE AN EXCLUSIVE INTERVIEW WITH TWO OF THE SENIOR FIGURES IN *R.A.I.D.* – THE GLOBAL AGENCY FOR *ROBOTICS ANALYSIS, INTELLIGENCE AND DEFENCE.*

FIRST, PLEASE WELCOME CHIEF SCIENTIFIC OFFICER, *DOCTOR NITA SHARMA!*

THANKS, YAHYA. GLAD TO BE HERE.

CLAP CLAP CLAP CLA

YOUR MUM IS SO COOL, ALEX. YOU'RE SO LUCKY!

REALLY?

DON'T YOU THINK SO?

I DUNNO. SHE'S MY MUM, Y'KNOW?

YES. YOUR *MUM* IS ONE HUNDRED TIMES COOLER THAN YOU.

HOW MUST THAT *FEEL?*

DOCTOR SHARMA, THE LAST FEW YEARS HAVE SEEN A RISING RATE OF ROBOT-ASSISTED CRIME AND TERRORISM INCIDENTS.

WELL, LIKE ANY TECHNOLOGY, ROBOTS CAN BE USED FOR GOOD OR EVIL...

BUT IT'S GETTING *WORSE,* ISN'T IT?

JUST THIS YEAR, LONDON HAS BEEN SUBJECT TO A SERIES OF ATTACKS FROM WHAT MANY ARE CLAIMING WAS AN INDEPENDENT, SELF-DIRECTED *ROBOTIC* INTELLIGENCE...

THE SO-CALLED *ROBOT 23.*

THAT... THAT'S...

DOCTOR SHARMA – ARE ROBOTS JUST GETTING OUT OF *HAND?*

...AND SO, UNLESS WE HAVE ANY FURTHER CHALLENGERS, THE TROPHY GOES TO ULTRA'S DESIGNERS...

GRAB!

WE ARE ROBOTI X

WITH AN 'X'!

AND WE ARE... THE FUTURE!

(CHECK OUT OUR VUTUBE CHANNEL FOR UPDATES AND BONUS CONTENT!)

OUR CREATIONS CAN DEFEAT ANYONE! AND WE SHALL PROVE IT!

HERE TODAY IN THE CROWD WE HAVE A VERY SPECIAL GUEST...

...A ROBOT DESIGNED BY DOCTOR ROBOTICUS HIMSELF – CREATOR OF THE LEGENDARY SUPER ROBO SEVEN!

OH NO.

WHAT?

FREDDY, WE SHOULD GO.

WHAT'S HAPPENING?

WE WILL CRUSH THE HANDIWORK OF ROBOTICUS...

AND PROVE OURSELVES TO BE THE GREATEST CYBERTECHNICIANS OF THE MODERN AGE!

(BUY OUR T-SHIRTS!)

WE CHALLENGE...

...YOU!

CHALLENGE YOU TO ULTIMATE ROBOTIC COMBAT!

WAIT, ARE YOU TALKING TO ME?

BECAUSE I AM SUPER INTO THIS IDEA.

MEANWHILE, IN THE AUDITORIUM...

...AS I SAY, ROBOTS ARE ONLY AS DANGEROUS AS THE PEOPLE WHO PROGRAM THEM.

THE BENEFITS THAT ROBOTS OFFER TO SOCIETY ARE ENORMOUS, BUT JUST LIKE ANY TECHNOLOGY, THERE WILL BE THOSE WHO ABUSE IT.

THE KIND OF INCIDENTS YOU MENTION JUST SHOW THE NEED FOR BETTER CONTROLS AND REGULATION – WHICH IS EXACTLY WHERE R.A.I.D. COMES IN...

WOW, YOUR MUM IS GETTING FEISTY.

I DIDN'T KNOW IT WAS GOING TO BE SO... HOSTILE.

AH, SHE CAN TAKE THIS CLOWN.

YOU'RE WRONG!

IT'S GONE TOO FAR!

WE HAVE ROBOTS WALKING AROUND NOW, WITH NO CONTROLS – POSING A REAL DANGER, TO REAL PEOPLE!

I'M SORRY, BUT THAT'S JUST NOT THE...

EXCUSE ME! I WAS STILL TALKING!

IT SHOULDN'T BE ALLOWED!

WHAT HAPPENS WHEN THEY START TO THINK FOR THEMSELVES? WHEN THEY TURN AGAINST US?

YOU SHOULD SHUT THEM DOWN! SHUT THEM ALL DOWN!

MEANWHILE, IN THE AUDITORIUM, THINGS ARE HEATING UP...

...ROBOTS

OUT OF CONTROL!

SHUT 'EM DOWN!

IF I MAY...

BARONESS FAROOQ, PLEASE.

THIS KIND OF *ALARMISM* IS *DEEPLY* UNHELPFUL.

WE CAN'T UNINVENT TECHNOLOGY. THE GENIE IS OUT OF THE BOTTLE.

OUR JOB AT R.A.I.D. IS TO *CONTROL* IT...

WHICH IS WHERE THESE GUYS COME IN...

MEET THE *PEACEKEEPERS.* THE LATEST 9-SERIES COMMANDO MECHS, FULLY CUSTOMISED FOR URBAN POLICING AND THE PROTECTION OF CIVILIANS.

EACH ONE IS VIRTUALLY UNSTOPPABLE IN COMBAT, AND SUBJECT TO THE STRICTEST CONTROLS AND COMMAND PROTOCOLS.

AND THESE ARE JUST PART OF AN *ARSENAL* OF WEAPONS AND RESOURCES R.A.I.D. CAN DEPLOY AROUND THE WORLD TO CONTAIN ANY ROBOTIC THREAT.

AH, THOSE GUYS AREN'T SO GREAT.

HEY. WHAT'S *THAT?*

WHAT?

LOOK – UP THERE IN THE SKY!

THERE'S SOMETHING – IT'S COMING IN *FAST* –

LET ME ASSURE YOU, YOU HAVE NOTHING TO FEAR.

R.A.I.D. ARE...

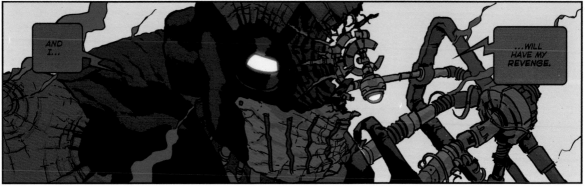

GO.

ALEX —

GO!

THAT BLAST — THAT WAS KERCHATOV PLASMA.

THAT'S NOT POSSIBLE!

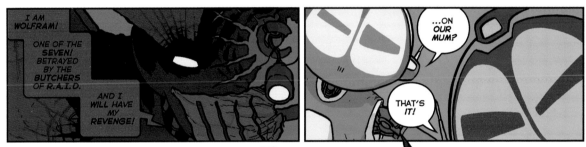

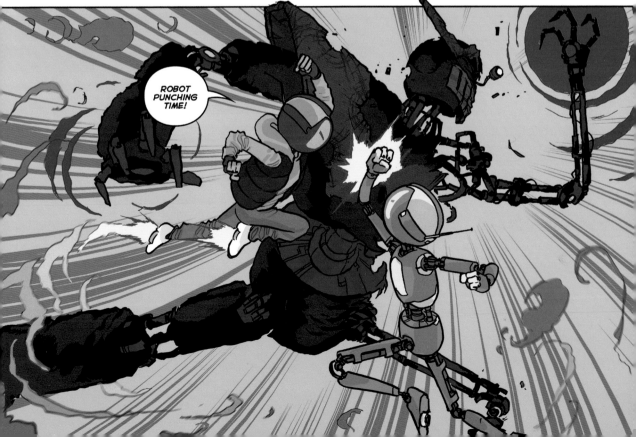

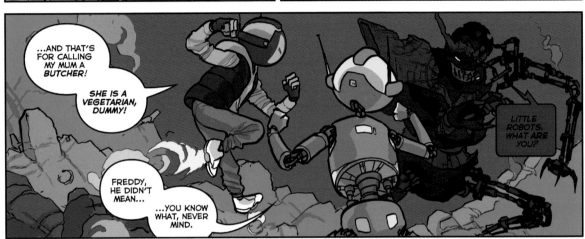

89

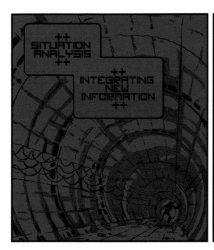

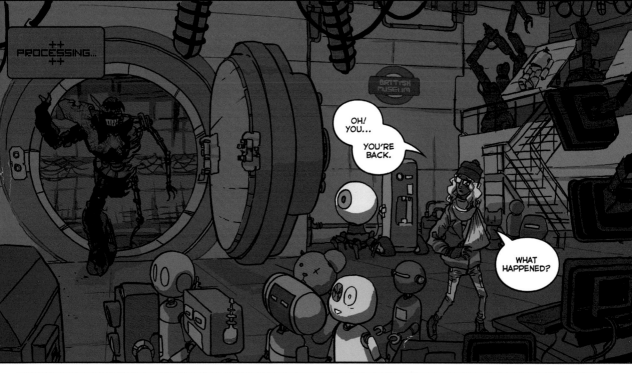

END OF BOOK 2